This book belongs to.......................

Carolyn Wells Edition of Mother Goose

Illustrated by . . . .   MARGIE

EMMONS

JANET ROBSON

SHARON STEARNS

DOLLI TINGLE

MADISON WOOD

KIPPY

PETER LOCKE

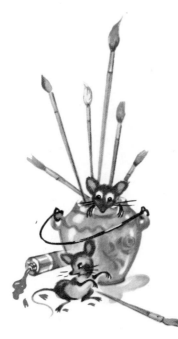

Printed in Singapore for the Publishers Peter Haddock Limited, Bridlington, England

THIS LITTLE PIG

This little pig went to market;
This little pig stayed home;
This little pig had roast beef;
This little pig had none;
This little pig said, "Wee, wee, wee!"
      all the way home.

HEY, DIDDLE, DIDDLE

Hey, diddle, diddle!
  The cat and the fiddle,
The cow jumped over the moon.
  The little dog laughed
To see such sport;
  And the dish ran away
    with the spoon.

LITTLE NANCY ETTICOAT

Little Nancy Etticoat
  In a white petticoat
And a red nose;
  The longer she stands
The shorter she grows.

GREAT A, LITTLE A

Great A, little a, bouncing B,
The cat's in the cupboard,
    and can't see me

She went to the barber's
  To buy him a wig,
And when she came back
  He was dancing a jig.

She went to the tailor's
  To buy him a coat,
And when she came back
  He was riding a goat.

OLD MOTHER HUBBARD

Old Mother Hubbard,
  She went to the cupboard,
To give her poor dog a bone;
  But when she came there
The cupboard was bare,
  And so the poor dog had none.

She took a clean dish
  To get him some tripe,
And when she came back
  He was smoking his pipe.

She went to the hatter's
  To buy him a hat,
And when she came back
  He was feeding the cat.

She went to the cobbler's
  To buy him some shoes,
And when she came back
  He was reading the news.

The dame made a curtsey,
  The dog made a bow;
The dame said, "Your servant,"
  The dog said, "Bow, wow!"

LITTLE BOY BLUE

Little Boy Blue,
    come blow your horn;
    The sheep's in the meadow,
        the cow's in the corn.
Where's the little boy
    who tends the sheep?
He's under the haystack fast asleep.
    Will you wake him? No, not I;
    For if I do he'll surely cry.

RIDE AWAY, RIDE AWAY

Ride away, ride away,
Johnny shall ride,
And he shall have pussy-cat
        Tied to one side;
And he shall have little dog
Tied to the other;
And Johnny shall ride
        To see his grandmother.

BOW, WOW, SAYS THE DOG

Bow, wow, says the dog;
Mew, mew, says the cat;
    Grunt, grunt, goes the hog;
    And squeak goes the rat.
Chirp, chirp, says the sparrow;
Caw, caw, says the crow;
    Quack, quack, says the duck;
    And what cuckoos say, you know.

So, with sparrows and cuckoos;
With rats and with dogs;
    With ducks and with crows;
    With cats and with hogs;
A fine song I've made
To please you my dear;
    And if it's well sung,
    'Twill be charming to hear.

A CAT CAME DANCING

A cat came dancing out of a barn,
  With a pair of bagpipes
    under her arm;
  She could sing nothing but,
    "Fiddle cum fee,
  The mouse has married
    the bumble-bee!"
  Pipe, cat; dance, mouse:
  We'll have a wedding at
    our good house.

PEASE PORRIDGE HOT

Pease porridge hot, pease porridge cold,
Pease porridge in the pot
    nine days old.

IF ALL THE WORLD

If all the world were apple pie,
  And all the sea were ink,
And all the trees were bread
    and cheese,
  What would we have to drink?

UP IN THE GREEN ORCHARD

Up in the green orchard
    there is a green tree,
The finest of pippins
    that ever you see;
The apples are ripe
    and ready to fall,
And Reuben and Robin
    shall gather them all.

GUSHY COW BONNY

Gushy cow bonny, give me thy milk,
And I will give thee a gown of silk —
A gown of silk and a silver tee —
If thou wilt give thy milk to me.

JACK SPRAT

Jack Sprat could eat no fat,
His wife could eat no lean;
And so it was, betwixt them both,
They licked the
platter clean.

OLD WOMAN OF LEEDS

There was an old woman of Leeds,
Who spent all her time in good deeds;
She worked for the poor
Till her fingers were sore,
This pious old woman of Leeds.

LITTLE WHITE MOUSE

Oh, what a sweet little white mouse!
Oh, what a dear little bright mouse!
With his eyes of pink, going winky-wink,
Oh, what a sweet little white mouse!

SMILING GIRLS, ROSY BOYS

Smiling girls, rosy boys,
Come and buy my little toys,
Monkeys made of gingerbread,
And sugar horses painted red.

AS I WAS GOING TO ST. IVES

As I was going to St. Ives,
I met a man with seven wives.

Every wife
had seven sacks;

Every sack had seven cats;

Every cat had seven kits.

Kits, cats, sacks and wives:
How many were going to St. Ives?

BOBBY SHAFTOE

Bobby Shaftoe's gone to sea,
Silver buckles on his knee;

He'll come back and marry me,
Bonny Bobby Shaftoe!

Bobby Shaftoe's young and fair,
Curly is his golden hair;
He's my love for evermore,
Bonny Bobby Shaftoe!

THE MULBERRY BUSH

Here we go 'round the mulberry bush,
The mulberry bush, the mulberry bush,

Here we go 'round the mulberry bush,
So early in the morning.

14

I HAD A LITTLE PONY

I had a little pony,
His name was Dapple Grey;
I lent him to a lady
To ride a mile away.

She whipped him, she lashed him,
She rode him through the mire;

BLESS YOU, BLESS YOU

Bless you, bless you, Burny Bee,
Say when will your wedding be?
If it be tomorrow day,
Take your wings and fly away!

I would not lend my pony now
For all the lady's hire.

TOMMY SNOOKS

As Tommy Snooks and Betsy Brooks
Were walking out one Sunday,
Said Tommy Snooks to Betsy Brooks,
"Tomorrow will be Monday."

T'OTHER LITTLE TUNE

T'other little tune, t'other little tune,

Prythee, Love,
Play me t'other little tune.

See-saw, Margery Daw,

He shall have but a penny a day

Johnny shall have a new master;

Because he can't work any faster.

THERE WAS A CROOKED MAN

There was a crooked man,
And he went a crooked mile;

He found a crooked sixpence
Against a crooked stile;

He bought a crooked cat

Which caught a crooked mouse;

And they all lived together
In a little crooked house.

HICKORY, DICKORY, DOCK

Hickory, dickory, dock,
The mouse ran up the clock;
The clock struck one,
And down he came,
Hickory, dickory, dock.

SULKY SUE

Here's Sulky Sue —
    What shall we do?
Turn her face to the wall
    Till she comes to.

HICKETY, PICKETY

Hickety, pickety, my black hen,
She lays eggs for gentlemen:

Sometimes nine and sometimes ten
Hickety, pickety, my black hen

FOR GENTLEMEN ONLY

ONE, TWO, BUCKLE MY SHOE

One, two,
Buckle my shoe;

Three, four,
Shut the door;

Five, six,
Pick up sticks;

Seven, eight,
Lay them straight;

Nine, ten,
A big fat hen;

Eleven, twelve,
Dig and delve;

Thirteen, fourteen,
Maids a-courting;

Fifteen, sixteen,
Maids a-kissing;

Seventeen, eighteen,
Maids a-waiting;

Nineteen, twenty,
That's a-plenty!

PUSSY SITS BESIDE THE FIRE

Pussy sits beside the fire —
How did she come there?

"How do you do, Miss Pussy,
Miss Pussy, how do you do?"

"In walks the little dog —
Says, "Pussy, are you there?"

"I thank you kindly, little dog,
I fare as well as you!"

POLLY,
PUT THE KETTLE ON

Polly, put the kettle on,
    Polly, put the kettle on,
Polly, put the kettle on,
    And we'll all have tea.

Sukey, take it off again,
    Sukey, take it off again,
Sukey, take it off again,
    They've all gone away.

JACK, BE NIMBLE

Jack, be nimble,
  Jack, be quick,
Jack, jump over the candlestick.

TOMMY TROT

Tommy Trot, a man of law,
Sold his bed and lay on straw,
Sold the straw and slept on grass,
To buy his wife a looking glass.

WHAT ARE LITTLE BOYS MADE OF?

What are little boys made of,
      made of,
What are little boys made of?
Snips and snails
      and puppydogs' tails;
That's what little boys
      are made of.

What are little girls made of,
      made of,
What are little girls made of?
Sugar and spice
      and all that's nice;
That's what little girls
      are made of.

SIMPLE SIMON

Simple Simon met a pieman,
      Going to the fair;
Said Simple Simon to the pieman,
      "Let me taste your ware."

Said the pieman to Simple Simon,
      "Show me first your penny."
Said Simple Simon to the pieman,
      "Indeed I have not any."

Simple Simon went a-fishing,
      For to catch a whale;
All the water he had there
      Was in his mother's pail.

RAIN, RAIN

Rain, rain, go away:
      Come again another day:
Little Suzy wants to play.

SING, SING

Sing, sing, what shall I sing?
      The cat's run away
            with the pudding-bag string!
Do, do, what shall I do?
      The cat has bit it
            quite in two.

TO MARKET, TO MARKET

To market, to market,
To buy a fat pig;
Home again, home again,
Jiggety, jig.

To market, to market,
To buy a fat hog;
Home again, home again,
Jiggety jog.

I HAD A LITTLE HEN

I had a little hen,
    The prettiest ever seen,
She washed up the dishes
    And kept the house clean.

She went to the mill
    To fetch me some flour;
She brought it back home
    In less than an hour.

She baked me my bread,
    She brewed me my ale;
She sat by the fire
    And told a fine tale.

LITTLE TOMMY TUCKER

Little Tommy Tucker,
Sing for your supper!
What shall I eat?
White bread and butter.
How shall I cut it
Without any knife?
How shall I marry
without any wife?

PAT-A-CAKE

Pat-a-cake, pat-a-cake, baker's man!
Make me a cake as fast as you can:
Pat it and prick it and mark it with T,
Put it in the oven for Tommy and me.

BOW, WOW, WOW

Bow, wow, wow,
Whose dog art thou?
Little Tom Tinker's dog,
Bow, wow, wow.

THE KING OF FRANCE

The King of France,
with twenty thousand men,
Went up the hill,
and then came down again.

POOR OLD ROBINSON CRUSOE

Poor old Robinson Crusoe!
Poor old Robinson Crusoe!
They made him a coat
Of an old nanny goat;
I wonder how they could do so!
With a ring a ting tang,
And a ring a ting tang,
Poor old Robinson Crusoe!

LITTLE BIRD

Once I saw a little bird
Come hop, hop, hop;
So I cried, "Little bird,
Will you stop, stop, stop?"

I was leaning out of the window
To say, "How do you do?"
When he shook his little tail,
And far away he flew.

LITTLE POLLY FLINDERS

Little Polly Flinders
    Sat among the cinders,
Warming her pretty little toes;
    Her mother came and caught her,
And whipped her little daughter
    For spoiling her
        nice new clothers.

THE MAN IN THE WILDERNESS

The man in the wilderness asked me
    How many strawberries
        grew in the sea?

I answered him, as I thought good,
    As many as red herrings
        grew in the wood.

RUB-A-DUB-DUB

Hey, rub-a-dub-dub,
    three men in a tub,
And who do you think were there?
The butcher, the baker,
    the candlestick maker,
And all had come from the fair.

GOOSEY, GOOSEY, GANDER

Goosey, Goosey, Gander,
    Whither dost thou wander?
    Upstairs and downstairs,
      And in my lady's chamber.

PETER, PETER

Peter, Peter, Pumpkin Eater,
    Had a wife and couldn't keep her.
He put her in a pumpkin shell,
    And there he kept her very well.

WEE WILLIE WINKIE

Wee Willie Winkie
    runs through the town,
Upstairs and downstairs
    in his nightgown,
Rapping at the window,
    crying through the lock,
"Are the children in their beds
    For now it's eight o'clock."

JOCKY WAS A PIPER'S SON

Jocky was a piper's son;
    He fell in love when he was young.
The only tune that he could play
    Was: Over the hills and far away.
Over the hills and a great way off,
And the wind will blow
                my topknot off.

GEORGIE PORGIE

Georgie Porgie, pudding and pie,
    Kissed the girls and made them cry;
When the boys came out to play,
    Georgie Porgie ran away.

DIDDLE-Y-DIDDLE-Y-DUMPTY

Diddle-y-diddle-y-dumpty,
    The cat ran up the plum tree,
Half a crown to fetch her down,
    Diddle-y-diddle-y-dumpty.

ROBERT BARNES

'Robert Barnes, fellow fine,
    Can you shoe this horse of mine?"
'Yes, good sir, that I can
    As well as any other man;
There's a nail, and there's a prod,
    And now, good sir,
                your horse is shod."

A was an angler,
      Went out in a fog;
   He fished all the day,
      And caught only a frog.

B was cook Betty,
      A-baking a pie
   With ten or twelve apples
      All piled up on high.

C was a custard
      In a glass dish,
   With as much cinnamon
      As you could wish.

D was fat Dick
   Who did nothing
            but eat;
   He would leave book
            and play
   For a nice bit of meat.

E was an egg
      In a basket with more
   Which Peggy did sell
      For a shilling a score.

F was a fox,
      So cunning and sly,
   Who looked at the hen roost,
      I need not say why.

G was a greyhound
      As fleet as you'll find,
   He ran in a race;
      Left all othe
            behind

H was a heron
   Who lived near a po
   Of standing on one l
      He was very fond.

I was the ice
      On which Billy did skate
      Till up went his heels
      And down went his pa

J was Joe Jenkins
   Who played on the fidd
   He began twenty tunes
   But left off in the middle.

K was a kitten
      Who jumped at a cork,
      And learned to eat m
      Without plate,
            knife, or fork.

L was a lark
      Who sang us a song,
      And waked us betim
   Lest we sleep too long.

M was Miss Molly
      Who turned in her toe
      And hung her head
         Till her knees
            touched her nose

N was a nosegay,
Sprinkled with dew,
Pulled in the morning,
And presented to you.

O was an owl
Who looked very wise;
He said, "Who-who!"
And blinked
his big eyes.

P was a parrot
With feathers like gold;
He never said more
Than he ever was told.

Q was the Queen
Who governed the land,
And sat on a throne
Very lofty and grand.

R was a raven,
Perched on an oak,
Who with a gruff voice
Cried, "Croak,
croak, croak!"

S was a stork
With a very long bill,
Who swallowed
down fishes
And frogs to his fill.

T was a trumpeter,
Blowing his horn,
Who told us the news
As we walked in the morn.

U was a unicorn
Who, it was said,
Wore an ivory bodkin
On his forehead.

V was a vulture
Who ate a great deal,
Devouring a dog
Or a cat at a meal.

W was a watchman
Who guarded the street,
Lest robbers or thieves
The good people
should meet.

X was King Xerxes
Who, if you don't know,
Reigned over Persia
A great while ago.

Y is the year
That is passing away,
And growing still shorter
With every day.

Z is a Zebra —
You've heard
that before;
And here ends my rhyme
Till I find you some more.

FROG WHO WOULD A-WOOING GO

A frog, he would a-wooing go,
    "Heigho," says Rowley,
Whether his mother would let him or
                                    no.

With a rowley powley,
            gammon and spinach,
    "Heigho," says Anthony Rowley!

So off he set with his opera hat,
    "Heigho," says Rowley,
And on the road he met with a rat.
With a rowley powley,
            gammon and spinach,
    "Heigho," says Anthony Rowley!

"Pray, Mr. Rat, will you go with me,"
    "Heigho," says Rowley,
"Kind Mrs. Mousey for to see?"
With a rowley powley,
            gammon and spinach,
    "Heigho," says Anthony Rowley!

When they reached the door of
Mousey's hall,
    "Heigho," says Rowley,
They gave a loud knock,
            and they gave a loud call,
With a rowley powley,
            gammon and spinach,
    "Heigho," says Anthony Rowley!

Pray, Mrs. Mouse, are you within?"
    "Heigho," says Rowley,
Oh, yes, kind sirs,
        I'm sitting to spin."
With a rowley powley,
        gammon and spinach,
    "Heigho," says Anthony Rowley!

'Pray, Mrs. Mouse, will you
        give us some beer?"
    "Heigho," says Rowley,
'For Froggy and I are fond of
        good cheer."
With a rowley powley,
        gammon and spinach,
    "Heigho," says Anthony Rowley!

'Pray, Mr. Frog, will you give us a
        song?"
    "Heigho," says Rowley,
'But let it be something
        that's not very long."
With a rowley powley,
        gammon and spinach,
    "Heigho," says Anthony Rowley!

"Indeed, Mrs. Mouse," replied Mr
            Frog,
    "Heigho," says Rowley,
"A cold has made me as hoarse as a
            hog."
With a rowley powley,
        gammon and spinach,
    "Heigho," says Anthony Rowley!
"Since you have caught cold,
        Mr. Frog," Mousey said,
    "Heigho," says Rowley,
"I'll sing you a song that I have just
            made."
With a rowley powley,
        gammon and spinach,
    "Heigho," says Anthony Rowley!

LITTLE BETTY BLUE

Little Betty Blue
   Lost her holiday shoe.
What shall little Betty do?
   Buy her another
   To match the other,
And then she'll walk in two.

SING SONG

Sing song, merry go round,
   Here we go up to the moon, oh,
Little Johnnie a penny has found,
   And so we'll sing a tune, oh!

"What shall I buy,"
    Johnnie did cry,
"With the penny I've found
    so bright and round?"

What shall you buy?
    A kite that will fly
Up to the moon,
    all through the sky.

A DILLER, A DOLLAR

A diller, a dollar,
  a ten o'clock scholar,
What makes you come so soon?
You used to come at ten o'clock,
  But now you come at noon.

LITTLE MISS MUFFET

Little Miss Muffet sat on a tuffet,
  Eating her curds and whey;
Along came a spider
  and sat down beside her,
And frightened Miss Muffet away.

BRYAN O'LIN

Bryan O'Lin had no breeches to wear,
So he bought him a sheepskin
  and made him a pair,

With the skinny side out
  and the woolly side in.
"Ah ha, that is warm!"
  said Bryan O'Lin.

The three little kittens
    found their mittens,
And they began to sing,
"Oh! Mother dear,
    see here, see here!
See, we have found our mittens."

"What! Found your mittens!
    You good little kittens!
Then you shall have some pie."
"Purr-r, purr-r,
    purr-r, purr-r."
"Then you shall have some pie."

THREE
LITTLE
KITTENS

Three little kittens
    lost their mittens,
And they began to cry,
"Oh! Mother dear,
    we sadly fear
That we have lost our mittens."

"Lost your mittens!
    You naughty kittens!
Then you shall have no pie."
Mee-ow, mee-ow,
    mee-ow, mee-ow."
"Then you shall have no pie."

The three little kittens
    washed their mittens,
And hung them up to dry;
"Oh! Mother dear,
    look here, look here!
See, we have washed our mittens."

"Washed your mittens!
    You clever kittens!
But I smell a rat close by.
Hush! Hush!"
    "Mee-ow, mee-ow,
We smell a rat close by."

The three little kittens
    put on their mittens,
And soon ate up the pie;
"Oh! Mother dear,
    we greatly fear
That we have soiled our mittens."

"Soiled your mittens!
    You naughty kittens!"
Then they began to sigh,
"Mee-ow, mee-ow,
    mee-ow, mee-ow,
Then they began to sigh.

THE QUEEN OF HEARTS

The Queen of Hearts,
She made some tarts,
All on a summer's day;

The King of Hearts
Called for the tarts,
And beat the Knave full sore;

The Knave of Hearts,
He stole the tarts,
And took them clean away.

The Knave of Hearts
Brought back the tarts,
And vowed he'd steal no more.

MY PRETTY MAID

"**W**here are you going,
   my pretty maid?"
"I'm going a-milking, sir,"
   she said.

"May I go with you,
   my pretty maid?"
"You're kindly welcome, sir,"
   she said.

"What is your father,
   my pretty maid?"
"My father's a farmer, sir,"
   she said.

"What is your fortune,
   my pretty maid?"
"My face is my fortune, sir,"
   she said.

"Then I can't marry you,
   my pretty maid!"
"Nobody asked you, sir,"
   she said.

OLD WOMAN
WHO LIVED IN A SHOE

There was an old woman
　　who lived in a shoe;
She had so many children,
　　She didn't know what to do.
She gave them some broth
　　without any bread;
She whipped them all soundly
　　and put them to bed.

I HAD A LITTLE NUT TREE

I had a little nut tree,
　　nothing would it bear
But a silver apple
　　and a golden pear;
The King of Spain's daughter
　　came to see me,
And all for the sake of
　　my little nut tree.
I skipped over water,
　　I danced over sea,
And all the birds in the air
　　couldn't catch me.

COCK'S ON THE HOUSETOP

The cock's on the housetop
      blowing his horn;
The bull's in the barn
      a-threshing the corn;

The maids in the meadow
      are making of hay:

The ducks in the river
      are swimming away.

RIDE A COCK-HORSE

Ride a cock-horse to Banbury Cross,
  To see a fine lady upon a white horse,

With rings on her fingers,
          and bells on her toes,
She shall have music
          wherever she goes.

HARK! HARK!

Hark! Hark! The dogs do bark;
  The beggars are coming to town,

Some in rags, some in tags,
  And some in velvet gowns.

BAA, BAA, BLACK SHEEP

Baa, baa, black sheep
    have you any wool?
Yes, sir, yes, sir,
    three bags full.

One for my master,
    and one for my dame,
And one for the little boy
    who lives in the lane.

A FARMER WENT TROTTING

A farmer went trotting
    Upon his grey mare,
Bumpety, bumpety, bump!
With his daughter behind him,
    So rosy and fair,
Bumpety, bumpety, bump!

PUSSY CAT

Pussy Cat, Pussy Cat,
    where have you been?
I've been to London
    to see the queen.

Pussy Cat, Pussy Cat,
    what did you there?
I frightened a little mouse
    under her chair.

OLD SOLDIER OF BISTER

There was an old soldier of Bister,
    Went walking one day
        with his sister,

When a cow at one poke
    Tossed her into an oak,
Before the old gentleman missed her.

RIDDLE-ME-REE

Riddle-me, riddle-me, riddle-me-ree,
Perhaps you can tell what
this riddle may be:

As deep as a house,

as round as a cup,

And all the king's horses
can't draw it up.

CHARLEY WAG

Charley Wag
Ate the pudding, and left the bag.

DAFFY-DOWN-DILLY

Daffy-down-dilly is
new come to town,
With a petticoat green,
and a bright
yellow gown.

Mary, Mary, quite contrary,
   How does your garden grow?

With silver bells and cockle shells,

And pretty maids all in a row.

IF WISHES WERE HORSES

If wishes were horses,
   Then beggars would ride;
If turnips were watches,
   I'd wear one by my side.

48

ONE MISTY,
MOISTY MORNING

One misty, moisty morning,
    When cloudy was the weather,
I chanced to meet an old man
    Clothed all in leather.

He began to compliment,
    And I began to grin —
How do you do,
    and how do you do,
    And how do you do, again?

OH WHITHER?

There was an old woman
    tossed up in a basket,
Seventy times as high as the moon.
What did she there
    I could but ask it,
For in her hand
    she carried a broom.

"Old woman, old woman,
    old woman," said I,
"Oh whither, oh whither,
    oh whither so high?"
"To sweep the cobwebs
    out of the sky,
And I shall be back again
    by and by."

COME HITHER

Come hither, little puppy dog;
   I'll give you a new collar
If you will learn to read your book,
   And be a clever scholar.

Come hither, pretty cockatoo;
   Come and learn your letters,
And you shall have a knife and for
   To eat with, like your betters.

"No, no!" replied the puppy dog,
   "I've other fish to fry,

"No, no!" the cockatoo replied,
   "My beak will do as well;
I'd rather eat my victuals thus
   Than go and

          learn to spell."

For I must learn to guard your house,
   And bark when thieves come nigh."

With a tingle, tangle, tit-mouse!
   Robin knows great A
And B and C and D and E,
        F, G, H, I, J, K.

With a tingle, tangle, tit-mouse!
   Robin knows great A
And B and C and D and E,
        F, G, H, I, J, K.

Come hither, little pussy cat;
  If you'll your grammar study,

I'll give you silver clogs to wear
  Whene'er the gutter's muddy.

"No! whilst I grammar learn,"
            says Puss,
"Your house will, in a trice,
Be overrun from top to bottom
  With flocks of rats
            and mice."

With a tingle, tangle, tit-mouse!
  Robin knows great A
And B and C and D and E,
            F, G, H, I, J, K.

Come hither, then, good little boy,
  And learn your alphabet,

And then a pair of boots and spurs
  Like Papa's you shall get.

"Oh, yes! I'll learn my alphabet;
  And when I well can read,

Perhaps Papa will give me, too,
  A pretty long-tailed steed."

With a tingle, tangle, tit-mouse!
  Robin knows great A
And B and C and D and E,
            F, G, H, I, J, K.

TWO OLD WOMEN

Oh, dear, what can the matter be?
Two old women
    up in an apple tree;
One came down,
    the other stayed there;
And said she wouldn't
    come down till
      Saturday.

THIRTY DAYS HATH SEPTEMBER

Thirty days hath
    September,
April, June and November.
All the rest have thirty-one,
Excepting February alone,
Which some years
    has twenty-eight,
But in leap year
    twenty-nine.

Fly away, Jack!
Fly away, Jill!

Come again, Jack!
Come again, Jill!

TWO BLACKBIRDS

There were two blackbirds
Sitting on a hill,

The one named Jack,

The other named Jill.

OLD KING COLE

Old King Cole was a merry old soul,
    And a merry old soul was he;
He called for his pipe,
        and he called for his bowl,
And he called for
            his fiddlers three.

Every fiddler had a fiddle,
    And a very fine fiddle had he;
Oh, there's none so rare
            as can compare
With King Cole and
            his fiddlers three.

TWO BIRDS

There were two birds,
        sat on a stone,
Fal de ral-al de ral-laddy.
One flew away, and
        then there was one,
Fal de ral-al de ral-laddy.

One of these little birds
        back again flew,
Fal de ral-al de ral-laddy.
The other came after, and
        then there were two,
Fal de ral-al de ral-laddy.

The other flew after, and then
        there was none,
Fal de ral-al de ral-laddy.
So the poor stone
        was left all alone,
Fal de ral-al de ral-laddy.

Says one to the other,
        "Pray how do you do?"
Fal de ral-al de ral-laddy.
"Very well, thank you,
        and pray how are you?"
Fal de ral-al de ral-laddy.

PUSSY CAT MOLE

Pussy Cat Mole
        jumped over a coal,
And in her best petticoat
        burnt a great hole.

Poor Pussy's weeping,
        she'll have no more milk

Until her best petticoat's
        mended with silk.

TOM, TOM, THE PIPER'S SON

Tom, Tom, the piper's son,
        Stole a pig, and away he run;
The pig was eat,
        and Tom was beat,
And Tom ran crying
        down the street.

MAN IN THE MOON

The man in the moon
came down too soon
And asked the way to Norwich.

He went by the south,
and burnt his mouth

FAT MAN OF BOMBAY

There was a fat man of Bombay
Who was smoking, one sunshiny day,
When a bird, called a snipe,
Flew away with his pipe,
Which vexed the fat
man of Bombay.

With eating cold pease porridge.

LITTLE TOMMY TITTLEMOUSE

Little Tommy Tittlemouse
    Lived in a little house;
He caught fishes
    In other men's ditches.

HEY DIDDLE DINKETTY

Hey diddle dinketty, poppetty pet,
The merchants of London wear scarlet;
Silk in the collar, and gold in the hem,
So merrily march the merchantmen.

BUZZ AND HUM

"Buzz," quoth the blue fly;
    "Hum," quoth the bee;
"Buzz" and "hum," they cry,
    And so do we.

BARBER, BARBER

Barber, barber, shave a pig;
    How many hairs will make a wig?
Four and twenty, that's enough;
    Give the barber a pinch of snuff.

THIS IS THE WAY THE LADIES RIDE

This is the way the ladies ride:
    Tri, tre, tre, tree,
    Tri, tre, tre, tree!

This is the way the gentlemen ride:
    Gallop-a-trot,
    Gallop-a-trot!
This is the way the gentlemen ride:
    Gallop-a-trot!

This is the way the ladies ride:
    Tri, tre, tre, tree,
    Tri, tre, tre, tree!

This is the way the farmers ride:
    Hobbledy-hoy,
    Hobbledy-hoy!
This is the way the farmers ride:
    Hobbledy-hoy!

I LOVE SIXPENCE

I love sixpence,
    pretty little sixpence,
I love sixpence
    better than my life;
I spent a penny of it,
    I spent another,
And I took fourpence
    home to my wife.

Oh, my little twopence,
    pretty little twopence,
I love twopence
    better than my life;
I spent a penny of it,
    I spent another,
And I took nothing
    home to my wife.

Oh, my little fourpence,
    pretty little fourpence,
I love fourpence
    better than my life;
I spent a penny of it,
    I spent another,
And I took twopence
    home to my wife.

Oh, my little nothing,
    my pretty little nothing,
What will nothing
    buy for my wife?
I have nothing,
    I spent nothing,
I love nothing
    better than my wife.

COME, LET'S TO BED

"Come, let's to bed,"
        says Sleepyhead;

"Put on the pan," says greedy Nan,

"Tarry awhile," says Slow.

"Let's sup before we go."

All the king's horses

HUMPTY DUMPTY

Humpty Dumpty sat on a wall,

And all the king's men

Humpty Dumpty had a great fall;

Couldn't put Humpty Dumpty together again.

MARY'S LAMB

Mary had a little lamb
  With fleece as white as snow;
And everywhere that Mary went
  The lamb was sure to go.

It followed her to school one day,
  Which was against the rule;
It made the children laugh and play
  To see a lamb at school.

And so the teacher turned it out
  But still it lingered near,
And waited patiently about
  Till Mary did appear.

"What makes the lamb love Mary so?"
  The eager children cried.
"Why, Mary loves the lamb, you know!"
  The teacher then replied.

THE MONTHS

January brings the snow,
Makes our feet and fingers glow.

February brings the rain,
Thaws the frozen lake again.

March brings breezes
loud and shrill,
Stirs the dancing daffodil.

April brings the primrose sweet,
Scatters daisies at our feet.

May brings flocks of pretty lambs,
Skipping by their fleecy dams.

June brings tulips, lilies, roses,
Fills the children's hands
with posies.

JANUARY ✻ FEBRUARY ✻ MARCH ✻ APRIL ✻ MAY ✻ JUNE

Hot July brings cooling showers,
Apricots and gillyflowers.

August brings the sheaves of corn,
Then the harvest home is borne.

Clear September brings blue skies,
Goldenrod, and apple pies.

Fresh October brings the pheasant,
Then to gather nuts is pleasant.

Dull November brings the blast,
Makes the leaves go whirling fast.

Chill December brings the sleet,
Blazing fire and Christmas treat.

A JOLLY MILLER

There was a jolly miller
  Lived on the river Dee.
He worked and sang
      from morn till night,
  No lark so blithe as he;

And this the burden of his song
  Forever used to be:
"I jump me jerrime jee!
  I care for nobody, no, not I,
Since nobody cares for me."

HOT CROSS BUNS

Hot cross buns!
  Hot cross buns!
One a penny, two a penny,
  Hot cross buns!

Hot cross buns!
  Hot cross buns!
If ye have no daughters,
  Give them to your sons!

CHARLEY WORLEY HAD A COW

Charley Worley had a cow,
Black and white
    about the brow;

Open the gate,
    and let her go through,
Charley Worley's old cow!

UPON MY WORD AND HONOUR

Upon my word and honour
As I was going to Bonner,

I met a pig
    without a wig,
Upon my word and honour!

THE NORTH WIND

The north wind does blow,
And we shall have snow,

And what will the robin do then?
Poor thing?

He'll sit in the barn,
And keep himself warm,
And hide his head under his wing.
Poor thing!

I LIKE LITTLE PUSSY

I like little Pussy,
        her coat is so warm,
And if I don't hurt her,
        she'll do me no harm.

I'll not pull her tail,
        or drive her away,
But Pussy and I
        very gently will play.

OH, DEAR

Oh, dear, what can the matter be?
Johnny's so long at the fair;

He promised to buy me
          a bunch of blue ribbons
To tie up my bonny brown hair.

HANDY-SPANDY, JACK-A-DANDY

Handy-spandy, Jack-a-dandy,
Loves plum-cake and sugar-candy.

He bought some at a grocer's shop,
And pleased, away went,
                    hop, hop, hop!

CURLYLOCKS

Curlylocks, Curlylocks,
　　wilt thou be mine?
Thou shalt not wash dishes
　　nor yet feed the swine,

But sit on a cushion
　　and sew a fine seam,
And feed upon strawberries,
　　sugar and cream.

NEEDLES AND PINS

Needles and pins, needles and pins,
When a man marries,
　　his trouble begins.

CACKLE, CACKLE, MADAM GOOSE

Cackle, cackle, Madam Goose!
   Have you any feathers loose?

Truly have I, little fellow,
Half enough to fill a pillow;
And here are quills,
               take one or ten,
And make from each a dandy pen.

ELIZABETH

Elizabeth, Elspeth, Betsy and Bess,
    They all went together
        to see a bird's nest.

They found a bird's nest
            with five eggs in,
    They all took one and left four in.

MOLLY, MY SISTER

Molly, my sister, and I fell out,
And what do you think
   it was all about?

She loved coffee, and I loved tea,
And that was the reason
   we couldn't agree.

LONDON
BRIDGE

London Bridge is
          falling down,
Falling down, falling down,

London Bridge is
          falling down,
My fair lady.

Off to prison she must go,
She must go, she must go,

Off to prison she must go,
My fair lady.

Index of Rhymes

Answers to Riddles

Index of Rhymes